# Hello Kitty's® Yearbook

## All-Year-Round Activities

by Bree and Drew Sieplinga

**SCHOLASTIC INC.**

New York   Toronto   London   Auckland   Sydney
Mexico City   New Delhi   Hong Kong   Buenos Aires

ISBN 0-439-56141-8

12 11 10 9 8 7 6 5 4 3 2

3 4 5 6 7 8/0

Printed in the U.S.A.
First printing, September 2003

Hello Kitty is a busy girl! She packs her days with family events, school activities, and an active social life. No matter what time of year it is, she always has a full schedule.

In this book, Hello Kitty will share her favorite things about each season. Along the way, there are groovy activities, scrumptious recipes, inspiring craft ideas, and cool stickers.

These pages are organized by month and season, but you can have fun doing the activities and crafts at any time of the year. Turn the page and jump into *Hello Kitty's Yearbook!*

# Fabulous Fall

Hello Kitty loves to watch the trees change into their colorful fall outfits. Hello Kitty and her friends also change their wardrobes in the fall. It's a must—the sun goes down earlier, the weather gets colder, and it's back-to-school time.

## Leaf It to Hello Kitty

Hello Kitty saves colorful, pretty fall leaves. To preserve a leaf, lay it flat between two paper towels and press it inside a big, heavy book. Leave it there for a few days. Here are ideas for displaying your fall leaves!

**Decorate your window.** Tape dried leaves on your window for a decoration that can be seen from both inside and out.

**Glue your leaves on colored paper.** Then hang them on your wall.

**Make a special fall box.** Use white glue to cover a shoe box with colored paper. Mix one teaspoon of water and one teaspoon of white glue in a disposable container. With a paintbrush, brush the mixture onto the underside of a leaf. Place the leaf on the box and then brush the mixture onto the top of the leaf, smoothing the leaf flat. The glue mixture will dry clear. Make different designs by using many colored leaves and arranging them in unique patterns—a border of small leaves around the top or sides of the box, or a circle of leaves on the top are two ideas.

# September

September means going back to school and seeing old friends, plus meeting new ones! Hello Kitty is excited about all of the new things she will learn in school this year. She knows that learning is fun and being smart is cool!

My friends and family who have birthdays in September are:

| Name | Date |
| --- | --- |
| _____ | _____ |
| _____ | _____ |
| _____ | _____ |

**Special days that are celebrated in September are:**

Labor Day                   First Monday
Grandparents' Day           First Sunday after Labor Day

_____                _____

_____                _____

_____                _____

## School Days

Hello Kitty likes to wear something special on her first day of school! Draw a picture of what you wore on your first day of school this year.

Getting new school supplies makes doing your homework fun! Make a list of the supplies you need here:

_____

_____

_____

_____

_____

_____

_____

_____

## Back-to-School Crafts

Spruce up your binder or notebook and make it your own by decorating the cover! Here are a few ideas:

**Make a collage.** Paste photos of you and your friends or other pictures that you like on your notebook or binder.

**Make sunflowers!** Dip a pencil eraser in brown paint. Use it to stamp a circle to be the center of the flower. Then use yellow paint to stamp petals around the center. (Be sure to wipe off the paint or use a different eraser when changing colors.)

**Add stickers or glitter.** This is an easy way to make your binder or notebook glamorous. You can even use Hello Kitty stickers from this book!

**Here are more craft ideas:**

**Get noticed with original book covers.** Cover your schoolbooks with brown paper (you can use either the roll kind or paper bags) and decorate them, too.

**Jazz up your hairdo!** Glue old buttons or ribbons on a barrette to make a new back-to-school accessory.

## Jody's Fun Facts

Wow your classmates with these fun September facts.

❀ Russians launched the first rocket to the moon on September 12, 1959.

❀ The world's average school year is 200 days. In the United States, it is 180. In Sweden, it's 170, and in Japan, 243.

❀ September is National Chicken Month.

❀ The first ice-cream cone was made, served, and eaten in New York City on September 22, 1886.

❀ September 16 is National Students Day.

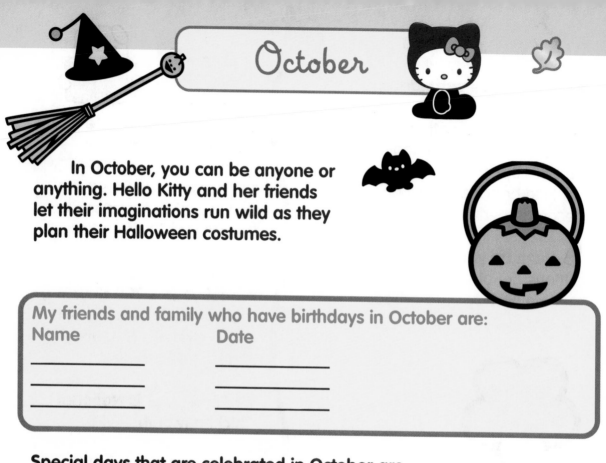

# October

In October, you can be anyone or anything. Hello Kitty and her friends let their imaginations run wild as they plan their Halloween costumes.

My friends and family who have birthdays in October are:

Name                          Date

_____            _____

_____            _____

_____            _____

**Special days that are celebrated in October are:**

National Children's Day          October 12
United Nations Day               October 24
Halloween                        October 31

_____            _____

_____            _____

_____            _____

## Brainstorm Your Costume

Dressing up for Halloween is a blast. But making and planning your costume is just as fun! Here are a few suggestions:

🦇 **Wacky style.** Find a crazy piece of clothing that you've always wanted to wear (like purple-and-yellow striped tights or long, silky gloves). Build your costume around that piece.

🦇 **Terrific themes.** Dress up with your friends around a theme—you could be the four seasons, a flock of birds, or your favorite music band.

🦇 **Timeless fashion.** Dress up as a hippie from the 1960s or a disco diva from the '70s. You and your friends could each wear a fashion from a different decade!

🦇 **Breathe life into an object.** Don't limit yourself to humans and animals. Dress up as a bubble-gum machine, a shampoo bottle, or the game of Twister!

9

## Costume Hunting

Hello Kitty finds costume accessories in all sorts of places. Here are some places you can look for creative costume ideas and props:

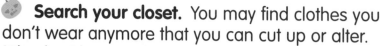 **Search your closet.** You may find clothes you don't wear anymore that you can cut up or alter. (Check with your parents before cutting or changing any clothes.)

**Explore the attic.** You may find hats, gowns, and things that can be used as costumes or props.

**Hunt in thrift stores.** They're full of inexpensive and unusual clothes.

**Accessorize.** In craft stores you'll find buttons, pom-poms, and beads to sew onto costumes.

Use this space to sketch costumes, paste inspiring clippings and pictures, or jot down Halloween ideas.

★ Trick-or-Treat Original

Decorate a brown paper bag with stickers, markers, cutout pictures, and glitter to make a candy-collecting bag that displays your own special style or goes with your costume.

# November

November is one of Hello Kitty's favorite months, probably because her birthday is November 1! On Thanksgiving, Hello Kitty thinks about all the things she is thankful for.

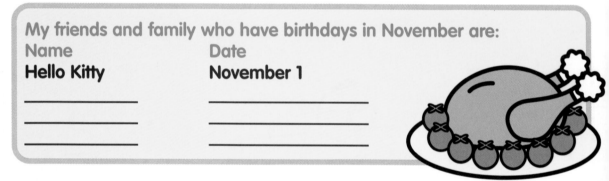

**My friends and family who have birthdays in November are:**

| Name | Date |
| --- | --- |
| **Hello Kitty** | **November 1** |
| _____ | _____ |
| _____ | _____ |
| _____ | _____ |

**Special days that are celebrated in November are:**

| | |
| --- | --- |
| **Veterans Day** | November 11 |
| **Thanksgiving** | Fourth Thursday |
| **Ramadan** | The ninth month of the Islamic lunar calendar |
| _____ | _____ |
| _____ | _____ |
| _____ | _____ |

## Bodacious Banana Bread

Here is Hello Kitty's banana bread recipe. Make this treat the day before Thanksgiving. Serve it for breakfast on Thanksgiving Day—that way your parents can focus on preparing the big meal.

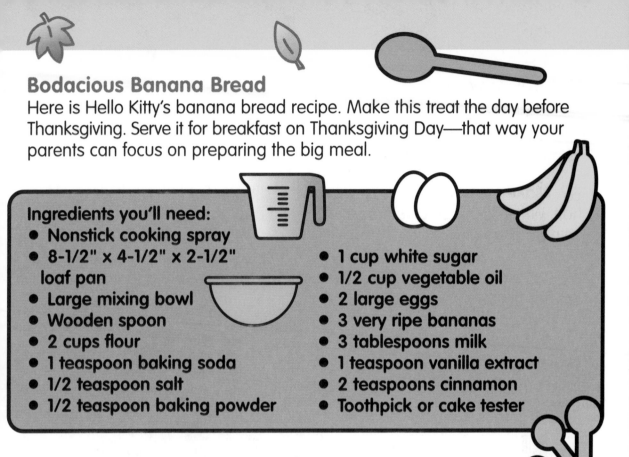

**Ingredients you'll need:**
- Nonstick cooking spray
- 8-1/2" x 4-1/2" x 2-1/2" loaf pan
- Large mixing bowl
- Wooden spoon
- 2 cups flour
- 1 teaspoon baking soda
- 1/2 teaspoon salt
- 1/2 teaspoon baking powder
- 1 cup white sugar
- 1/2 cup vegetable oil
- 2 large eggs
- 3 very ripe bananas
- 3 tablespoons milk
- 1 teaspoon vanilla extract
- 2 teaspoons cinnamon
- Toothpick or cake tester

First, find an adult to help you make this delicious treat. Preheat the oven to 350°F. Spray the loaf pan with the cooking spray. In the mixing bowl, combine all the ingredients. Stir the mixture until it is creamy with no lumps. Pour the batter into the pan. Bake for about an hour, or until you can stick a toothpick in the middle and it comes out clean. Let it cool for a half hour before eating. Yummy!

## Helpful Kitty

Thanksgiving is a time of food, family, and fun! Hello Kitty is a divine cook and helps out with Thanksgiving dinner. Here are other ways to show your thankfulness:

❀ **Make place cards for Thanksgiving dinner.** Fold 3- x 5-inch cards in half. Write each person's name on a card and then decorate the cards with markers and stickers.

❀ **Tell someone you are for thankful for them.** Make a thanksgiving card or note.

❀ **Volunteer.** Find ways to help others in your community. Maybe you can donate food or toys to a charity or visit people at a nursing home.

❀ **Collect pennies.** At the end of the month, send the money you've collected to a charity that you care about. Ask your family and friends to do the same!

# Wish Scroll

A wish scroll keeps your dreams close to your heart.

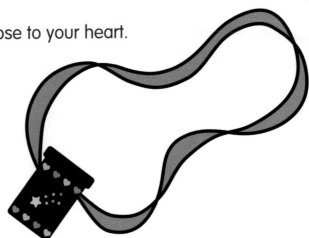

**Things you will need:**
- Craft knife
- 1 empty, plastic film canister
- 1 36-inch length of ribbon, cord, or very heavy thread
- 2 pony or wooden beads
- Pencil
- 1 one-inch-wide strip of paper
- Stickers

1. Have an adult use a craft knife to help you make two holes in the film canister—one on each side, near the top.

2. Thread the ribbon through one hole and out the other. Make sure that there is an equal length of ribbon on each side of the film canister. Then string a bead onto each end of the ribbon. Secure each bead with a knot in the ribbon.

3. On the paper, write your wishes. Then roll the paper like a scroll, put it inside the canister, and place the lid on the canister. Decorate it with stickers.

4. Tie the ends of the string so that it fits around your neck.

# Wonderful Winter

In the winter, Hello Kitty heads outside to ice-skate and make snow angels. Afterward, she snuggles up with a good book and a cup of hot cocoa. Hello Kitty's family is very important to her, so she also looks forward to cozy holiday celebrations at this time of year.

## Kathy's Cozy Cocoa for Two

Hello Kitty's best friend, Kathy, makes hot cocoa when Hello Kitty visits. You can make some, too, with her recipe. It will make enough for two people—you and a friend!

**Ingredients you'll need:**
- 2 tablespoons cocoa
- 2 tablespoons sugar
- Pinch of salt
- Small saucepan
- 2/3 cup water
- 1-1/3 cup milk

Find an adult to help you make this delicious treat. Mix the cocoa, sugar, and salt in the saucepan. Slowly stir the water in. Heat and stir the mixture over medium heat until it boils. Boil for two minutes, stirring constantly. Add milk and heat until hot. Pour into two mugs and serve.

Add a special twist to your cocoa!
**Put a candy cane or a cinnamon stick in each mug and stir. Or drop in orange rind for a touch of citrus.**

# December

December is a time when Hello Kitty gets together with her family to celebrate the holidays. She loves to hear how her friends and their families celebrate this time of year.

My friends and family who have birthdays in December are:

Name

Date

_____     _____

_____     _____

_____     _____

**Special days that are celebrated in December are**

Kwanza                    December 26–January 1

Hanukkah                  Hanukkah changes every year—
                          check your calendar!

Christmas                 December 25

_____     _____

_____     _____

# Timmy and Tammy's Popsicle-stick Frame

Timmy and Tammy made Hello Kitty
a special picture frame with
a picture of the three of
them inside. Put pictures
of you and your friends
in these homemade frames
and give one to each of
your friends for
a personalized gift.

## Things you will need:

- 7 Popsicle sticks (some craft stores sell colored ones)
- White glue
- 4-inch piece of string or ribbon
- Glitter, paint, beads, or markers
- Safety scissors
- Photograph or picture to put in the frame

1. Lay down two Popsicle sticks. One will be the
top of your frame and one will be the bottom.

2. Take two more Popsicle sticks and lay them on top of the first two to form a square. Glue them in place.

3. Take two more Popsicle sticks. Put them in the same position as your first two Popsicle sticks and glue them in place.

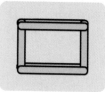

4. Glue one more Popsicle stick flat on the bottom of the frame, to keep your picture from falling out.

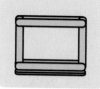

5. Glue a small loop of string or ribbon on the back of your picture frame so you can hang it on the wall.

6. Use glitter, paint, beads, or markers to decorate your frame. You can also use found items, such as shells, pretty stones, and acorns.

## Apple-licious Wrapping Paper
Your friends and family won't want to unwrap their gifts!

**Things you will need:**
- Knife
- 1 apple
- Poster paint
- 2 disposable bowls
- A roll of brown paper

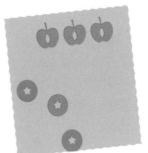

1. With an adult's help, slice the apple in half. For apple-shaped prints, slice the apple in the same direction as the core. For a circle-shaped print with a star in the center, slice your apple horizontally.

2. Choose two paints and pour each into its own bowl.

3. Dip a half apple in poster paint and stamp it on the brown paper in any pattern you like. Then dip the other half apple in another color. Continue stamping. Use red and green for Christmas, blue for Hanukkah, or whatever colors you like.

**Make a wreath design. Use green paint to stamp a ring shape to form the wreath. Let the green paint dry. Then cut a sponge into a triangle and dip it in red paint. Stamp two triangles at the top of the wreath to make a bow.**

21

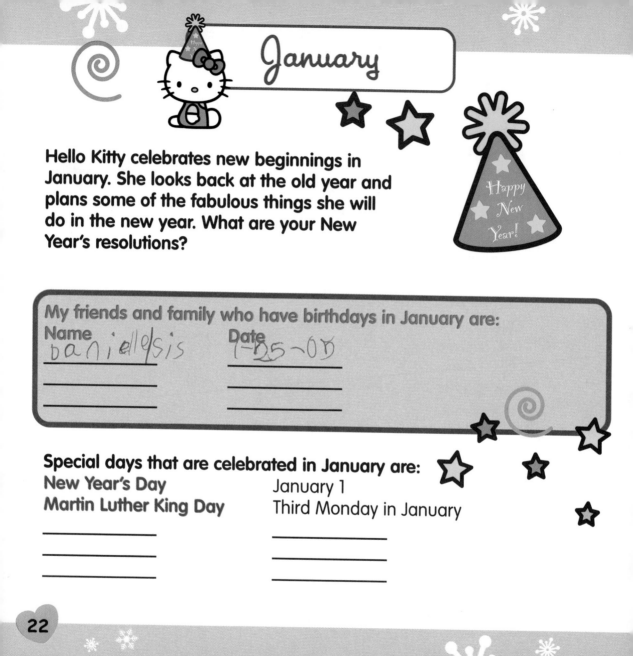

# January

Hello Kitty celebrates new beginnings in January. She looks back at the old year and plans some of the fabulous things she will do in the new year. What are your New Year's resolutions?

*Happy New Year!*

**My friends and family who have birthdays in January are:**

| Name | Date |
|------|------|
| Daniellesis | 7-25-00 |
| | |
| | |

**Special days that are celebrated in January are:**

New Year's Day          January 1
Martin Luther King Day   Third Monday in January

## Mimmy's Snowflake Decorations

Hello Kitty's twin sister, Mimmy, decorates her windows with these snowflakes in January. They stick to any shiny surfaces like refrigerators or windows.

**Things you will need:**
- Plastic wrap (a piece that's large enough to cover the snowflake pattern on the next page)
- Dimensional fabric paint (the kind that squeezes out of a bottle. It can be found in any craft store.)
- Glitter

1. Lay the plastic wrap over the snowflake pattern on the next page.

2. On the plastic wrap, trace the snowflake pattern with the fabric paint.

3. While the paint is still wet, sprinkle glitter over it. Then carefully shake off any excess glitter.

4. Let the snowflake dry completely, which should take about thirty minutes. Then peel it off the plastic wrap.

5. Stick your snowflake to your window and let it snow!

## Bubble Bath Day Spa

Bubble Bath Day is January 8. In January, treat yourself to a Bubble Bath Spa with these great spa ideas.

**Take a long, hot bubble bath.** Add fragrant bath salts or bath oil to the water to make your skin feel soft.

**Treat yourself to an egg-and-cucumber facial.** Put egg white on your face and cold slices of cucumbers on your eyes. Let the egg mask dry and then wash it off with warm water.

**Paint your toenails a radiant color.** A bright pink or red will bring a little sunshine to the cold, winter days.

**Use a creamy, scented lotion on your skin.** Skin tends to dry out in the wintertime, so it's important to moisturize.

**Put on cozy clothes or pajamas and relax with a good book.** A perfect end to your busy day!

# February

Hello Kitty's friends are important to her all year long, but on Valentine's Day, she celebrates how special they are to her. February is the shortest month of the year, but it sure is packed with fun!

My friends and family who have birthdays in February are:

Name                          Date

_____          _____
_____          _____
_____          _____

**Special days that are celebrated in February are:**

Groundhog Day          February 2
Valentine's Day          February 14
Presidents' Day          Third Monday

_____          _____
_____          _____
_____          _____

# Fifi's Heart-Shaped Valentine's Day Brooch
Fifi makes these valentine brooches for her friends.

## Things you'll need:
- Saucepan
- 1 cup flour
- 1 cup warm water
- 2 teaspoons cream of tartar
- 1 teaspoon vegetable oil
- 1 cup salt
- Red food coloring
- Bowl
- Brooch pins (you can find these in any craft store)
- Clear nail polish

1. In the saucepan, combine flour, water, cream of tartar, oil, and salt. With an adult's help, stir the mixture over medium heat until it's smooth.

2. Add two drops of red food coloring. Stir until the color is even.

3. Remove the mixture from the pan. Put it in a bowl to let it cool. Then knead the cooled dough until it's well blended.

4. Shape the dough into hearts and press a brooch pin into the back of each heart. When it's completely dry, brush it with clear nail polish. Beautiful!

# Swinging Spring

Hello Kitty swings into spring! When the flowers pop up and the birds return, Hello Kitty and her friends start hanging out outside again. What's your favorite thing about spring?

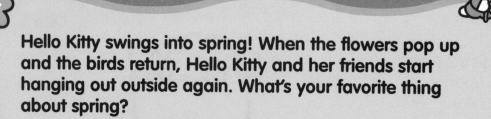

## Her-story

March is Women's History Month. Who is the woman you admire most? Is she your mother, a woman in history, a sports star, an actress, or a politician? Find out more about your woman hero by reading books about her or even interviewing her. You can also research on the Internet: Search online encyclopedias or type the woman's name into a search engine. Use this space to write what you discover.

_____

_____

_____

_____

_____

_____

_____

_____

_____

## Edible Dirt

Here's a fun spring treat that tastes way better than it looks! Hello Kitty surprised her friends by serving "edible dirt" at her last spring fling party.

**To serve you and a friend, you'll need:**
- 2 9-ounce clear plastic cups
- 2 scoops of chocolate ice cream, softened
- Chocolate cookie crumbs (crumble about 6 cookies)
- Gummy worms (as many as you'd like!)

1. Fill each plastic cup with a scoop of softened chocolate ice cream.

2. Top the ice cream with chocolate cookie crumbs.

3. Place gummy worms in the "dirt," serve immediately, and enjoy!

## Outrageous Outings

Now that the weather's warmer, it's time to go out on the town! Grab some friends and…

**Design a museum scavenger hunt.** Have an adult go to an art museum and make a list of details found in paintings. Then you and your friends have to find and write down the names of the paintings!

**Bird-watch.** Get a book from the library about the birds that live in your part of the country. Find an inexpensive pair of plastic binoculars, grab a notebook, and go to a park or a nature reserve. Keep a log of all the birds you spot.

**Host a potluck picnic.** Invite your friends and ask everyone to make a different food. Bring Frisbees, a soccer ball, and other sports equipment to guarantee a good time!

**Have a photo shoot.** All you need is a camera! Find fun locations—a park, the playground, or the mall are all good ideas. Then take pictures of you and your friends striking poses!

# April

One of the best things about Hello Kitty is her sense of humor. She wishes that every month started like April—with a joke!

My friends and family who have birthdays in April are:

| Name | Date |
| --- | --- |
| _____ | _____ |
| _____ | _____ |
| _____ | _____ |

**Special days that are celebrated in April are:**

| April Fool's Day | April 1 |
| --- | --- |
| Earth Day | April 22 |
| _____ | _____ |
| _____ | _____ |

## A Passion for Poetry

April is National Poetry Month. Poems can express feelings, describe a scene, or tell a story. Hello Kitty especially likes to write haiku, a type of Japanese poetry. Try writing your own haiku:

1. Think of a subject. It can be anything—your favorite animal, your best friend, your favorite food. Write a list of the words to describe your subject.

2. Use your words to write three lines. The first and third lines have five syllables. The second line has seven syllables.

Here is an example of a haiku.

### Spring
Winter chased away
Short-sleeved shirts and birds return
Warm breeze surrounds me

Use this space to write your own haiku.

_____

_____

_____

_____

## Tippy's Terrarium

In the spring, Tippy plants his garden. You can plant almost any kind of seed in this homemade terrarium.

**Things you will need:**
- 1 2-liter plastic soda bottle with cap
- Very sharp scissors or craft knife
- Dirt or potting soil
- Flower seeds
- Water

1. Wash and rinse out the bottle and cap. Remove the label from the bottle.

2. Ask an adult to cut off the side of the bottle where the label was.

3. Fill the cutoff bottom with dirt or potting soil.

4. Plant flower seeds in the dirt and add water.

5. Put the cap on the top of the bottle and place it over the bottom. You will have to work a bit to get the edges of the top to fit inside the bottom.

6. Put your terrarium in a sunny spot and be patient.

7. When your plants grow big enough, replant them in a bigger pot or in your garden.

**Tracy's Comic Relief**

**What kind of music do rabbits like?**
*Hip-hop*

**What do you get from confused chickens?**
*Scrambled eggs*

**What did the duck say to the waitress?**
*Just put it on my bill!*

**Why did the pony take cough medicine?**
*He was a little hoarse.*

39

# May

In May, Hello Kitty knows that summer is just around the corner. If April showers did their work, there will be flowers in May!

My friends and family who have birthdays in May are:

Name | Date
--- | ---
_____ | _____
_____ | _____
_____ | _____

**Special days that are celebrated in May are:**

| | |
| --- | --- |
| May Day | May 1 |
| Cinco de Mayo | May 5 |
| Mother's Day | Second Sunday |
| Memorial Day | Fourth Monday |
| _____ | _____ |
| _____ | _____ |
| _____ | _____ |

## Mother, May I?

On Mother's Day, Hello Kitty likes to make Mama White feel special. Celebrate your mother or other important women in your life. You could…

🌸 give her a back rub.

🌸 write her a poem.

🌸 read her a story.

🌸 make her a cup of tea.

🌸 share some chocolate or candy.

🌸 do an extra chore around the house.

🌸 pick her some wildflowers.

🌸 help her prepare a meal.

## May Flowers

May flower magnets will brighten your locker or refrigerator.

### Things you will need:
- Pencil
- Craft foam sheets in various colors
- Safety scissors
- Tacky glue (available at craft stores)
- Magnet

1. Using a pencil, draw the shape of a flower on a foam sheet. A sunflower works well, but use your creativity! Then, using the safety scissors, cut it out.

2. Next, draw the middle of the flower and cut it out.

3. Glue the flower's center onto the flower.

4. Glue the magnet on the back and let it dry completely.

# Pretty Pincushion

One Mother's Day, Hello Kitty gave Mama White a homemade pincushion. You can make it as a gift for someone, too!

**Things you will need:**
- Empty, clean tuna or cat food can
- Water
- Juice of 1 lemon
- Cotton balls
- Safety scissors
- One 6" x 6" piece of decorative cotton fabric
- Ribbons, lace, fabric, construction paper, or buttons
- Craft glue

1. Wash the can using water and lemon juice. The lemon juice will help remove any odors. Then fill the can with as many cotton balls as you can.

2. Cut a fabric circle one inch larger than the can's diameter.

3. Cover the cotton balls with the circle. Tuck the edges into the can. Then carefully glue the fabric to the inside top edge of the can and let it dry.

4. Decorate the outside of the can with ribbons, lace, etc.
Use your pincushion as a decoration. Or take up sewing and wow everyone with your amazing creations!

# Swell Summer

School's out for summer! Hello Kitty counts down the days until summer vacation begins. Finally it's here and she's ready to pack her days full of outdoor activities, sleepovers, trips out of town, parties, and all the things that make summer so swell.

## Summer Box

Every summer, Mama White helps Hello Kitty put together a special box full of arts-and-crafts supplies. Whenever Hello Kitty feels the need to create, she gets out her summer box. Make your own summer box and fill it with:

Glue
Construction paper
Safety scissors
Glitter
Stickers
Tape
String and ribbon
Feathers, sticks, shells
Markers
Crayons
Paints and paintbrushes
…and anything else you need to make stupendous summer art!

**Make your own summer gallery. Find a place in the house or in your room to display all of your summer creations.**

# June

It's summertime and the living is easy! Now that Hello Kitty has finished school, she can lie back and relax, spend time with her friends, and enjoy the long summer days.

My friends and family who have birthdays in June are:

| Name | Date |
| --- | --- |
| _____ | _____ |
| _____ | _____ |
| _____ | _____ |

**Special days that are celebrated in June are:**

| Father's Day | Third Sunday |
| --- | --- |
| Flag Day | June 14 |
| _____ | _____ |
| _____ | _____ |
| _____ | _____ |

## Slumber Party Extravaganza

Hello Kitty loves to host (and attend!) summertime slumber parties. She finds that one way to make slumber parties unique is to come up with a theme. Here are some of Hello Kitty's favorite slumber party themes:

**Film Festival.** Rent your favorite videos and have everyone dress up as their favorite movie character.

**Sticker Swap.** Have every guest bring one sheet of stickers for every girl. At the party, swap! Everyone goes home with a new supply of stickers.

**Beauty Divas.** Spoil one another with manicures, hairdos, makeovers, and facials.

**Cookie Craze.** With an adult's help, bake two or three types of cookies at your party. Then send each guest home with her own bag of cookies!

Make invitations that express the theme of your party.

If you choose to host the Film Festival slumber party, cut out pictures of movie stars and glue one on the back of each invitation.

Include a sticker strip with each Sticker Swap invitation.

The Beauty Divas invite can be sealed with a kiss! Put on some lipstick and "kiss" each invitation.

For the Cookie Craze party invitation, with an adult's help make a large cookie for each of your guests. Use white icing to write the time and date of the party on the top. Yum!

# Get in Shape, Girl!

Hello Kitty stays fit by thinking of fun and easy ways to exercise. So get off the couch, turn off the TV, and…

🌸 take the stairs.

🌸 arrange a day hike or even a weekend hiking trip in a state park.

🌸 plan a roller-skating night with friends.

🌸 learn a martial art.

🌸 take a yoga class or rent a yoga video with your friends.

🌸 take a walk or a run with your dog.

🌸 swim laps at a local pool.

# July

In July, Hello Kitty declares her independence. Now's the time to run barefoot through the grass and sip lemonade!

**My friends and family who have birthdays in July are:**

| Name | Date |
| --- | --- |
| _____ | _____ |
| _____ | _____ |
| _____ | _____ |

**A special day that is celebrated in July is:**

**Independence Day**     July 4

_____     _____

_____     _____

_____     _____

## I Dream of Ice Cream

To cool down and celebrate one of the best treats ever during Ice-cream Month, host an ice-cream party!

Here's how it works: Assign each guest a different topping to bring. You supply the ice cream. Then each guest can build her own sundae exactly the way he or she likes it.

Of course there are the usual toppings: caramel, hot fudge, nuts, whipped cream, cherries, and sprinkles. Here are some unusual topping ideas:

- Coconut flakes
- Crushed cookies
- Crushed ice-cream cones
- Dry cereal
- Granola
- Jam
- Marshmallows
- Powdered cocoa mix

51

## Bird Breakfast

In July, beautiful birds flit around the sky. Create this bird feeder to make some feathered friends of your own.

**Things you will need:**
- Cookie cutters
- Stale piece of bread or a piece of toast
- String
- Peanut butter
- Birdseed or sunflower seeds

1. Use a cookie cutter to cut the bread into a shape.

2. Poke a small hole in the bread. Put a piece of string through the hole and tie the ends together.

3. Spread a thin layer of peanut butter on both sides of the bread.

4. Then sprinkle birdseed or sunflower seeds on the peanut butter. Hang the bird breakfast in a tree, from your porch, or outside your window, and wait for your friends to fly in.

## For Your Eyes Only

During the summer, Hello Kitty sends Thomas letters, notes, and e-mails to keep in touch. When Hello Kitty has a top secret message for Thomas, she uses their secret code. Use this code to write secret messages to your friends.

*from Thomas*

| A | B | C | D | E | F | G | H | I | J | K | L |
|---|---|---|---|---|---|---|---|---|---|---|---|
| 13 | 14 | 15 | 16 | 17 | 18 | 19 | 20 | 21 | 22 | 23 | 24 |

| M | N | O | P | Q | R | S | T | U | V | W | X | Y | Z |
|---|---|---|---|---|---|---|---|---|---|---|---|---|---|
| 25 | 26 | 1 | 2 | 3 | 4 | 5 | 6 | 7 | 8 | 9 | 10 | 11 | 12 |

Practice by decoding this message from Hello Kitty:

16-4-17-13-25    14-21-19    13-26-16
18-1-24-24-1-9    11-1-7-4    20-17-13-4-6.

# August

In August, things really heat up. Hello Kitty and her friends cool down by going to the beach or running through a backyard sprinkler. August is also a time when Hello Kitty goes on vacation with her family. Whether she's traveling the world or exploring her own neighborhood, Hello Kitty enjoys each and every day.

My friends and family who have birthdays in August are:

| Name | Date |
|------|------|
| _____ | _____ |
| _____ | _____ |
| _____ | _____ |

**Special days that are celebrated in August are:**

| Friendship Day | First Sunday |
|----------------|--------------|
| **Be an Angel Day** | August 22 |
| _____ | _____ |
| _____ | _____ |
| _____ | _____ |

## Friendship Day Beaded Bracelet

On Friendship Day, make your friend a beaded bracelet. Use bead colors from the list below to show your friend what you admire most about her or him.

**Generous=Orange**
**Loyal=Blue**
**Kind=Pink**
**Smart=Green**
**Cheerful=Yellow**
**Fun=Red**

### Things you'll need:
- Elastic beading cord
- Cut crystal, glass, or plastic beads
- Clear nail polish

1. Cut a piece of cord about 6 inches long.

2. Using the colors you've chosen, string the beads onto the cord in any pattern you'd like. Size the bracelet to fit your friend's wrist.

3. Tie the ends together securely. After trimming the cord, seal the end with clear nail polish.

## Sudsy Angel Soap

On Be an Angel Day, show your friends how special they are by making them luxurious soap.

**Things you will need:**
- Newspaper
- Knife
- 1 bar of glycerin soap
- Three microwavable cups
- Potholder or oven mitt
- Candy molds
- Plastic spoon
- Plastic bags
- Ribbon or pretty cord

1. Cover your work area in newspaper and have an adult help you cut the bar of glycerin soap into three pieces. (One bar will make three soaps.) Put one piece in each cup.

2. Microwave the cups on high for 15 seconds or until the soap is completely melted. Use a potholder or oven mitt to remove the cups from the microwave—they'll be hot!

3. Using a plastic spoon, stir the soap. Then have an adult help you quickly pour the liquid soap into your molds.

4. Let the soap cool and harden. Once it's hardened, carefully pop each one out of the mold. If you choose to give the soap as a gift, place a few in a clear plastic bag and tie the bag shut with a ribbon or pretty cord.

**Places to Go, People to See**
Hello Kitty loves to travel. She's been all around the world and has learned about people of all different cultures. Where do you dream of traveling? Write a list of the places you'd like to visit.

_____     _____

_____     _____

_____     _____

_____     _____

# Fun All-Year-Round

With a schedule as packed as Hello Kitty's, it is particularly important for her to keep track of all of her special days and appointments.

Even when things seem hectic, you can keep your life organized by using a calendar or date book. You can make your own with markers and a ruler. (Check another calendar to make sure that you fill in the dates correctly.) You can also download calendar pages from the Internet to print out and decorate. Or you can use a ready-made calendar or date book.

Once you have your calendar, make good use of it by...

📷 transferring the birthdays of your friends and family and other special days from the month pages in this book.

📷 using the Hello Kitty calendar stickers in this book to mark special days.

📷 marking important events like vacations, tests, travel plans, and sleepovers.

Kathy's Birthday!

Sun.
Mon.
Tue.
Wed.
Thu.
Fri.
Sat.

## Celebrate Good Times

There is always somebody celebrating a birthday. Hello Kitty loves parties and likes to host birthday celebrations for herself and her friends. Host your own Hello Kitty party. Here are ideas to get you started:

**Design your own invitation.** Cut paper in the shape of Hello Kitty's head.

**Make party bows.** Follow Hello Kitty's fashion sense by having your guests wear bows. Take pieces of cloth or colored napkins and put a ponytail holder around each one. Then tie each piece of cloth or napkin in a knot to make a bow.

**Give each of your guests Hello Kitty party favors.**

**Make Hello Kitty cupcakes.** Have your guests decorate their cupcakes to look like Hello Kitty and her friends.

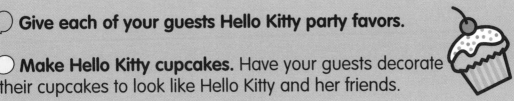

**Be a diva hostess like Hello Kitty.** Have plenty of snacks, movies, and games on hand. Make sure that everyone is included in the fun!

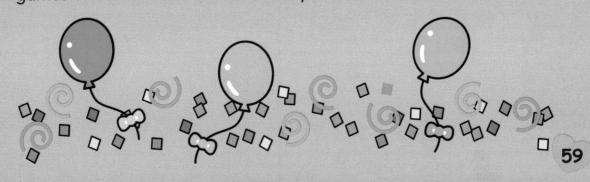

## Stargazing

Your astrological sign is based on which stars were in the sky during the month you were born. Hello Kitty is a Scorpio. Which sign are you and your friends?

**Capricorn**
December 22–January 20
Responsible, patient, and disciplined

**Aries**
March 21–April 20
Active, generous, and courageous

**Aquarius**
January 21–February 19
Independent, inquisitive, and idealistic

**Taurus**
April 21–May 21
Determined, affectionate, and trustworthy

**Pisces**
February 20–March 20
Sensitive, artistic, and compassionate

**Gemini**
May 22–June 21
Versatile, spontaneous, and charming

Cancer

June 22–July 23
Intuitive, imaginative, and nurturing

Leo

July 24–August 23
Dramatic, exuberant, and charismatic

Virgo

August 24–September 23
Analytical, dependable, and sincere

Libra

September 24–October 23
Gracious, thoughtful, and diplomatic

Scorpio

October 24–November 22
Intense, mysterious, and passionate

Sagittarius

November 23–December 21
Honest, curious, and optimistic

## Moon Bathing

Hello Kitty loves gazing at the moon. To our eyes, the moon seems to grow (wax) or shrink (wane). Here are the phases the moon goes through approximately every twenty-eight days. Check the newspaper or a lunar calendar and then mark the full moons and new moons on your calendar.

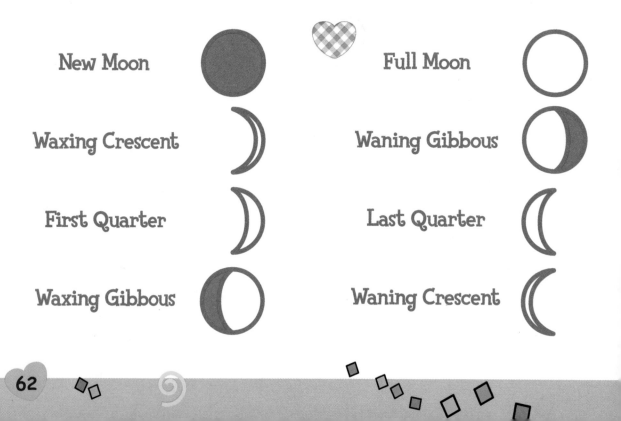

New Moon

Waxing Crescent

First Quarter

Waxing Gibbous

Full Moon

Waning Gibbous

Last Quarter

Waning Crescent

To My
Best Friend